CARL LARSSON
COLORING BOOK

Carl Larsson (1853–1919) was a Swedish artist who painted many portraits and book illustrations, but he is remembered above all for the watercolor paintings he made of his wife and children at home. He could paint an empty room, or he might paint a room crowded with kids in fancy costumes. Carl's wife, Karin, was an artist too, and their house was full of flowers, books, and painted furniture designed by the two artists.

You will find twenty-two of Carl Larsson's pictures in this coloring book. They are shown as small pictures on the inside front and back covers. When you color in the line drawings, you could copy the originals or you could try out some color combinations of your own. For instance, the white dress Martha Winslow is wearing in picture number 8 might be red when you're done coloring it! We've left the last page of this coloring book blank so that you can make a picture of your own—maybe of *your* favorite room?

Pomegranate

All works of art are from the collection of the Nationalmuseum, Stockholm.

1. *By the Cellar,* 1917. Watercolor on paper, 74 x 52.5 cm (29⅛ x 20¹¹⁄₁₆ in.).

2. *The Kitchen,* from the series *A Home,* 1898. Watercolor on paper, 32 x 43 cm (12⅝ x 16¹⁵⁄₁₆ in.).

3. *Daddy's Room,* from the series *A Home,* 1894–1897. Watercolor on paper, 32 x 43 cm (12⅝ x 16¹⁵⁄₁₆ in.).

4. *Lisbeth Reading,* 1904. Watercolor, charcoal, and tempera on paper, 60 x 76 cm (23⅝ x 29¹⁵⁄₁₆ in.).

5. *Breakfast Under the Big Birch,* from the series *A Home,* 1896. Watercolor on paper, 32 x 43 cm (12⅝ x 16¹⁵⁄₁₆ in.).

6. *In the Corner,* from the series *A Home,* c. 1895. Watercolor on paper, 32 x 43 cm (12⅝ x 16¹⁵⁄₁₆ in.).

7. *A Day of Celebration,* from the series *A Home,* c. 1895. Watercolor on paper, 32 x 43 cm (12⅝ x 16¹⁵⁄₁₆ in.).

8. *Martha Winslow as a Girl,* 1896. Watercolor on paper, 59.5 x 38 cm (23⁷⁄₁₆ x 14¹⁵⁄₁₆ in.).

9. *The Veranda,* from the series *A Home,* 1896–1897. Watercolor on paper, 32 x 43 cm (12⅝ x 16¹⁵⁄₁₆ in.).

10. *The Studio, One Half,* from the series *A Home,* 1894–1897. Watercolor on paper, 32 x 43 cm (12⅝ x 16¹⁵⁄₁₆ in.).

11. *Letter Writing,* 1912. Watercolor on paper, 52.5 x 74 cm (20¹¹⁄₁₆ x 29⅛ in.).

12. *Crayfishing,* from the series *A Home,* 1897. Watercolor on paper, 32 x 43 cm (12⅝ x 16¹⁵⁄₁₆ in.).

13. *Convalescence,* 1899–1902. Watercolor on paper, 52 x 66 cm (20½ x 26 in.).

14. *Old Anna,* from the series *A Home,* 1896. Watercolor on paper, 32 x 43 cm (12⅝ x 16¹⁵⁄₁₆ in.).

15. *Esbjörn at the Study Corner,* 1912. Watercolor on paper, 63 x 95 cm (24¹³⁄₁₆ x 37⅜ in.).

16. *Flowers on the Windowsill,* from the series *A Home,* 1894. Watercolor on paper, 32 x 43 cm (12⅝ x 16¹⁵⁄₁₆ in.).

17. *Brita's Forty Winks,* from the series *A Home,* 1894. Watercolor on paper, 32 x 43 cm (12⅝ x 16¹⁵⁄₁₆ in.).

18. *Between Christmas and New Year,* from the series *A Home,* 1896. Watercolor on paper, 32 x 43 cm (12⅝ x 16¹⁵⁄₁₆ in.).

19. *Lisbeth Angling,* from the series *A Home,* 1898. Watercolor on paper, 32 x 43 cm (12⅝ x 16¹⁵⁄₁₆ in.).

20. *The Dining Room,* from the series *A Home,* 1894–1897. Watercolor on paper, 32 x 43 cm (12⅝ x 16¹⁵⁄₁₆ in.).

21. *When the Children Have Gone to Bed,* from the series *A Home,* 1894–1897. Watercolor on paper, 32 x 43 cm (12⅝ x 16¹⁵⁄₁₆ in.).

22. *Cozy Corner,* from the series *A Home,* c. 1894. Watercolor on paper, 32 x 43 cm (12⅝ x 16¹⁵⁄₁₆ in.).

Pomegranate Communications, Inc.
19018 NE Portal Way, Portland OR 97230
800 227 1428   www.pomegranate.com

Distributed by Pomegranate Europe Ltd.
Unit 1, Heathcote Business Centre, Hurlbutt Road
Warwick, Warwickshire CV34 6TD, UK
[+44] 0 1926 430111
sales@pomeurope.co.uk

© 2010 Nationalmuseum, Stockholm
Line drawings © Pomegranate Communications, Inc.

Catalog No. CB117
Designed by Susan Koop
Printed in Korea

24 23 22 21 20 19 18 17 16 15   12 11 10 9 8 7 6 5 4 3

1. *By the Cellar*

2. The Kitchen

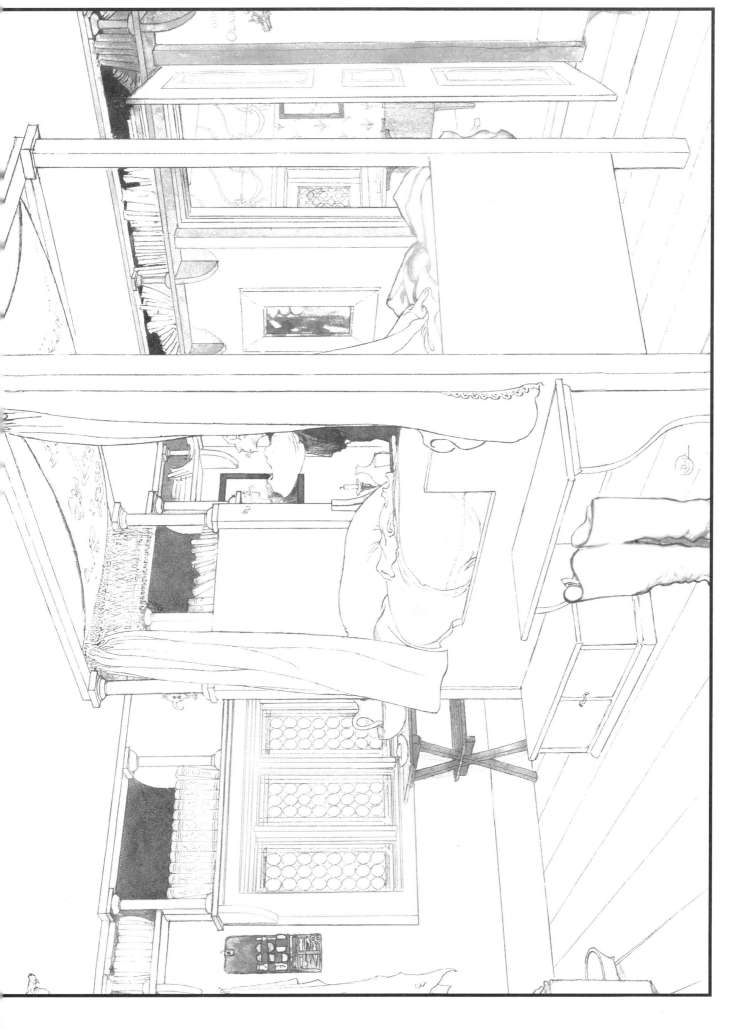

3. Daddy's Room

4. Lisbeth Reading

5. *Breakfast Under the Big Birch*

6. In the Corner

7. A Day of Celebration

8. *Martha Winslow as a Girl*

9. *The Veranda*

10. *The Studio, One Half*

12. *Crayfishing*

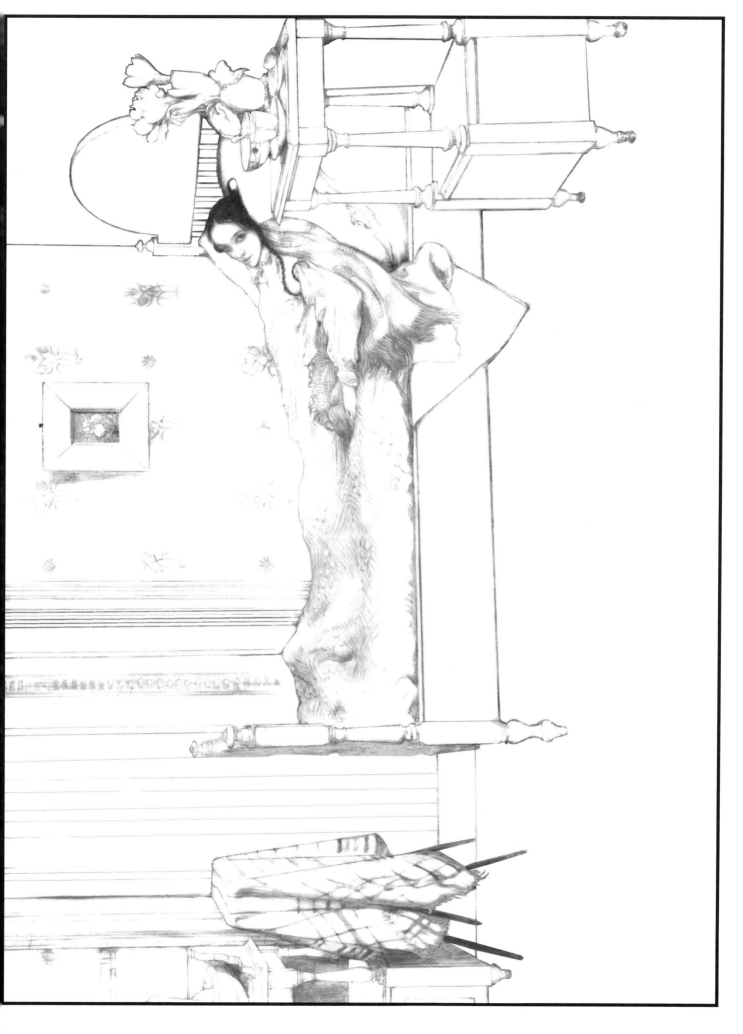

13. *Convalescence*

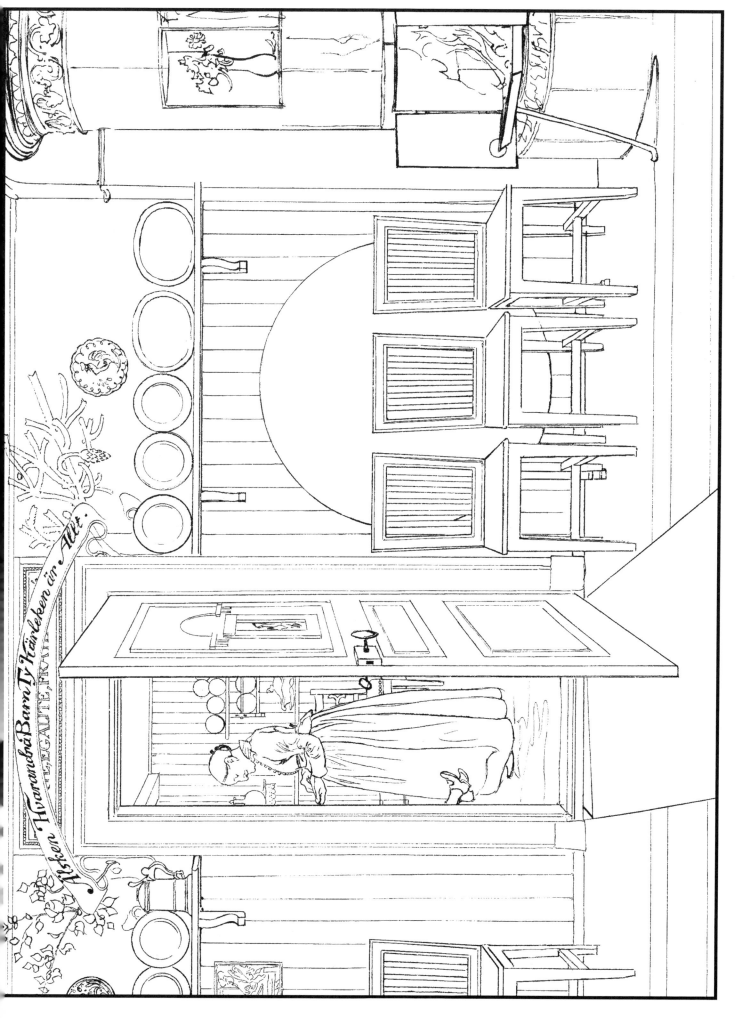

14. Old Anna

15. *Esbjörn at the Study Corner*

16. *Flowers on the Windowsill*

17. Brita's Forty Winks

18. *Between Christmas and New Year*

19. *Lisbeth Angling*

20. The Dining Room

21. *When the Children Have Gone to Bed*

22. Cozy Corner

Draw and color your own picture here!